The Yoga Manifesto

Our Books

Bhagavad Gita
Gheranda Samhita
Hatha Yoga Pradipika
Kamasutra
Shiva Samhita
Yoga Manifesto

The Yoga Manifesto

Brian Dana Akers

YogaVidya.com

YogaVidya.com, PO Box 569, Woodstock NY 12498-0569 USA

YogaVidya.com and *Read the Originals* are trademarks of
YogaVidya.com LLC.

First edition

⊗ The paper used in this book meets the requirements of the
American National Standards Institute/National Information
Standards Organization Permanence of Paper for Publications
and Documents in Libraries and Archives, ANSI/NISO
Z39.48-1992.

ISBN 978-0-9899966-9-3 (pbk. : alk. paper)
ISBN 978-0-9899966-8-6 (ebk.)

United Kingdom
A catalogue record for this book is available from the
British Library.

United States
A catalog record for this book is available from the
Library of Congress.

Loretta has patience.

To Jeanette, Ardith & Helen

Contents

Introduction   ix

Yoga and History   1

Yoga and Money   15

Yoga and Religion   21

Yoga and Science   25

Yoga and Society   31

Yoga and the Future   37

Author   49

Introduction

This is *The Yoga Manifesto*. It answers two questions: Why Yoga? Why now?

I will summarize the very long and remarkable history of Yoga from its Indian origins to its global present, its entanglement with money, where it fits in the constellation of religions, its dialectic with science, its place in today's society, and the bright future of Yoga. I believe that increasing the Yoga community's self-awareness, clarity of thought, and purity of motive will benefit the entire world.

This manifesto draws on current and classic scholarship, and my long, thoughtful life. I started Yoga at the age of 12—and I'm now well past

62!—so more than half a century. I also tapped the expertise of Dr. Madhav M. Deshpande (linguist), Dr. James D. Neill (astrophysicist), and Dr. Thomas R. Trautmann (historian). The improvements are theirs; the remaining short-comings are mine.

The word "yogis" includes yoginis. "India" refers to the entire subcontinent, that is, all of South Asia, not just the current Republic of India. I felt concluding each chapter with a verse from the *Hatha Yoga Pradipika* would bring the chapter to a satisfying close, rather like a colophon in a Sanskrit text. More notes and references are available at YogaVidya.com.

Let's dig in.

Yoga and History

So how are we to know the ancient yogis? They lived a very long time ago, at the beginning of recorded history.

Did they live in a high-tech Vedic super-civilization, a kind of Indian Wakanda? Were they speaking a Dravidian language? Did they practice asanas in the Indus Valley civilizations of Mohenjo Daro and Harappa, or even earlier? Probably not. Why not definitely not? Let's briefly consider sources, attestation, and chronologies.

What did the ancient yogis create that are now sources for us? Our first instinct is to go to our computers and visit their websites, read their blogs, and watch their videos. Of course, they produced none of these digital things. Nor did they produce analog radio, television, or motion pictures. They did not even produce printed books, magazines, or newspapers.

They did produce oral stories and tales, which would circulate, evolve, and persist even into modern times. More fixed are inscriptions on enduring hard surfaces, such as on temple walls, pillars, coins, stelae, copper plates, or pottery. But the mother lode would be manuscripts, in Sanskrit and other languages, written on palm leaves or inscribed into birch bark. If deemed important, these manuscripts would typically be recopied every few centuries by patient and dutiful scribes.

As for attestation, generally the farther back we go in time, the less evidence we have to work with, and the beginning of recorded history is very far indeed. Alas, we have no excavation sites containing high-tech specimens, nor Dravidian Yoga texts from 25 centuries ago, so those claims are unattested. We do have a smidgen of evidence from the Indus Valley civilizations, but that bit, the Pashupati seal, may or may not have anything to do with Yoga, so that claim is more contested than attested.

As for chronologies, Indic materials are notoriously imprecise. It is not uncommon for a text to be pinned down to a century—plus or minus one or two centuries! So a bit of humility is in order.

With those caveats in mind, what can we say about India and Yoga in those five or so centuries before the start of the Common Era? The subcontinent was more heavily forested, much less polluted, and a bit cooler. Elephants and tigers abounded; bees and birds buzzed and called. People were shorter (and shorter-lived), but just as smart and certainly less distracted than today. It was an agrarian economy of fixed villages, not a pastoral one of nomads. Travel was by foot and animal power on land; by oar and the wind in your sails on rivers and along the coasts. Pilgrimages slowed or paused during the monsoon.

Even though the world as a whole was much more lightly populated, perhaps only one to two percent of today's total, India was one of the few centers of population growth. This era is called the Second Urbanization (the Indus Valley civilizations being the first). Like today, the dislocations and changes in perspective brought on by urbanization and the speeding up of human history were enough to spark new modes of thinking, namely the ascetic movements.

The locus of Yoga was probably among speakers of Indo-Aryan languages in the central Gangetic region, what is nowadays eastern Uttar Pradesh and Bihar, what was then Magadha and adjacent polities, and later the Mauryan empire. The earliest yogis shared the same milieu as the Buddhists and the Jains in a pluralist society of renunciates, performing ascetic practices in the forests. Some were seeking rebirth in heaven and others liberation from rebirth itself. The word Yoga starts popping up here and there in various Upanishads.

Moving on to the first millennium of our current era, Indian civilization flourished. Temples, castles, and fortifications were constructed; magnificent sculptures and paintings were commissioned; sublime poetry, dramas, and music were composed. The pinnacle was the Gupta empire, which many scholars consider India's classical or golden age or even the *Pax Guptana*. This model of kingship spread overseas, notably to Southeast Asia. We also have our first two major Yoga texts, the *Bhagavad Gita* and the *Yoga Sutras*, both of which can sustain a lifetime of study.

The different parts of the *Gita* were composed orally, probably between the third century BCE and the second century CE. YogaVidya. com has published an edition that includes the Bhandarkar Oriental Research Institute's critical edition, which takes all of the different versions into account. Reading the *Gita*, one can't help but notice that the word Yoga is multivalent—it has a wide and deep semantic field. Indeed, the word becomes wildly multivalent over time, which is why I am not defining it in this manifesto.

The *Yoga Sutras*, written before the fifth century CE, is mostly devoted to recondite matters of existence, consciousness, and cognition, but it also introduces the iconic ashtanga, or eight-limbed, path of Yoga: yama, niyama, asana, pranayama, pratyahara, dharana, dhyana, and samadhi. This is today's most well-known division of the path of Yoga.

As we leave the first millennium and enter the medieval period, we find borrowings from Tantra and alchemy, and practices and texts that we recognize as the beginning of Hatha Yoga, (which in turn was the beginning of modern Yoga): asanas, kumbhakas, mantras, bandhas, mudras; nadis, chakras, and other features of a subtle anatomy; a multiplicity of texts with a multiplicity of opinions; and the most widely known text and author, the *Hatha Yoga Pradipika* by Svatmarama.

It's fascinating to note that the Daoist practice of Qigong, with its microcosmic orbit, predates and informs Hatha Yoga. The terms and conceptual structures are different, but I believe the underlying processes are the same, and that chi and prana are synonyms. Rather than translating Hatha Yoga as an instrumental compound, as "Yoga done with force," one could instead translate Hatha Yoga as a genitive compound, as "the Yoga of the force."

Yes, just like in *Star Wars*.

Next come the Europeans and their voyages of exploration, conquest, and conversion in the Early Modern period. The discovery of the New World by the Old initiates the Columbian Exchange of just about everything—plants, animals, people, metals, diseases, ideas, and more. What would our dosas and samosas be like without potatoes? Our curries without chilies? Perish the thought! Precious metals from Latin

America topped off the royal treasuries of India. Jesuits and other scholars began learning about the history and culture of India. The Asiatic Society was founded in Calcutta in 1784, and in 1786 Sir William Jones, working with Indian pandits, posited a common source for Sanskrit, Latin, and Greek, initiating the field of comparative linguistics. In the Indo-European world, vernacular languages took their places alongside Latin, Persian, and Sanskrit.

Undoubtedly the most amazing thing about Yoga and yogis for these three centuries was their response to the chaos and danger of the wars among the Mughals, the Marathas, the British, the French, and everybody else: yogis also militarized.

First in small bands, then by the hundreds, (and eventually employed in set-piece battles in formations of tens of thousands), yogis excelled in surprise raids, often at night, fighting in close quarters with spinning iron disks (chakras) flung from a sling. Completely naked, their bodies were rubbed with oil, which made them slippery to seize. Accustomed to physical discipline and exposure to the elements, the yogis operated like modern guerrillas, melting away into the countryside and extracting support from the local population. They lived beyond caste and social convention, beyond the reach of British law and the pounding hooves of Mughal heavy cavalry. They took hostages, engaged in intrigue, switched sides whenever it benefited themselves, yet regarded themselves as saints. Unsurprisingly, they acquired a sketchy reputation.

With the nineteenth century and the dawn of our current modern era, it's almost as if the world was thrown into a blender. Coal power, steamships, railroads, the telegraph, electrification, typewriters, phonographs, light bulbs—the list goes on and on. The advances in transportation and communications allowed the world to come to Yoga, and Yoga to flow out to the world.

Yoga flowed out into a complicated environment. Scholarship flowed out of Calcutta and into Europe, creating the Oriental Renaissance and fueling Romanticism. In America, Yoga flowed into a frothy mix of Transcendentalists, New Thought enthusiasts, revivalists, occultists, apparitionists, mesmerists, spiritualists, astrologers, psychics, mediums, voodoo priestesses, witches and sorcerers, and so on without end. Indian philosophy was a big part of the mix and Yoga was a small part. Theosophists internationalized this mix and brought it to India. Vivekananda's two visits to the West capped off the century.

Although the nineteenth century has the first wave of decolonization (Latin America, following the United States and Haiti), it was mostly a century of colonization. The British tightened their grip on India throughout the century, and in fact, the nineteenth century is often called the British Century or the *Pax Brittanica*. The armed yogis were brought to heel by law and by force and by pensioning them off. Indians took up English education voluntarily and involuntarily. Hindu reform movements, attempting to counter the Christian missionaries, adopted some of their practices and beliefs. Yogis were looked down on as frauds, vagrants, and rascals. It's a bit of a low point for Yoga on the subcontinent.

The first half of the twentieth century brought us the First World War, a second wave of decolonization (in Eastern Europe after the defeat of the Central Powers), the Great Depression, the Second World War, the atom bomb, and the partition of British India into India and Pakistan as independent states. The twentieth is often called the American Century.

In America, Yoga mostly continued to be part of the occult milieu or an example of the exotic East. Traveling "yogis" would rent hotel ballrooms for public lectures, place newspaper advertisements, and draw large audiences. For a fee, they would also teach smaller classes, tell fortunes, and perform magic tricks. Affluent white women were the target demographic.

In India, Yoga took quite a different path, drawing from the physical fitness movement, gymnastics, and science. Four individuals stand out. Shri Yogendra (1897–1989) and Swami Kuvalayananda (1883–1966) each founded institutions, conducted scientific research on Yoga, and published books and journals, thereby starting the modernization of Yoga. Swami Sivananda (1887–1963) and Krishnamacharya (1888–1989) each trained a cadre of students (Swamis Vishnudevananda, Satchidananda, Chidananda, and others for Sivananda; B. K. S. Iyengar, K. Pattabhi Jois, T. K. V. Desikachar, and others for Krishnamacharya) who would later spread over the globe and teach thousands of students, who would in turn teach millions of students. I am in Sivananda's lineage simply by chance—my teacher in Kalamazoo, Janet Bhuyan, was a student of Swami Vishnudevananda.

So by 1950 Yoga had survived, but little did

anyone realize that it was about to thrive. Before we look at Yoga today, let's get the fraught topics of money, religion, and science out of the way.

युवा वृद्धोऽतिवृद्धो वा व्याधितो दुर्बलोऽपि वा ।
अभ्यासात्सिद्धिमाप्नोति सर्वयोगेष्वतन्द्रितः ॥

One succeeds in all Yogas through energetic practice—even if one is young, old, very old, sick, or weak.

Yoga and Money

A fundamental attribute of Yoga is that it is
FREE. Once you know how to do it, you don't
need fancy clothing (anything comfortable will
do), special mats (I use a carpet remnant), an
awesome room (even florescent lights and lino-
leum floors will serve), intricate contraptions of
props, a vast library, the world's most famous
teacher, or an exotic locale. Any small flat space
will do. You can do it indoors or outdoors. You
can do it clothed or nude. (Probably best if not
outdoors *and* nude.) Yoga is FREE.

But since we all live in the highly monetized
economies of the twenty-first century, it would
be prudent to go through some of the ways to

not lose money from Yoga, to make a small amount of money, to make a lot of money, and to make a stupendous amount of money.

To not lose money, let's first consider what the economists call opportunity costs. If you are spending time and money on Yoga, you are not spending them on something else. Your alternative courses of action could be more or less lucrative, more or less costly, more or less enjoyable, more or less healthy, more or less moral. Since Yoga is good for you in so many ways, the chances are high that the opportunity costs are low. But Yoga is not for everyone, so at some point, you may feel it's best for you to stop and try something else.

A second cost to consider is teacher training courses. I took a six-week TTC in 1976 with a direct disciple of Sivananda. It was a wonderful experience. But TTCs can be surprisingly expensive, and they graduate far, far more teachers than there are teaching positions. It is very unlikely there will be a salaried, full-time-with-benefits position waiting for you, and much more likely that you will need to piece together classes here and there as a freelancer.

Third, avoid cults and scams. They can ruin your life and drain your bank balance. More on this in the next chapter.

To save a small amount of money with Yoga, the most important consideration is the least amenable to calculation, namely the health benefits. Yoga will almost certainly improve your health and well-being, but there is no way of knowing what your health and well-being would've been without it. It's definitely a positive—maybe large, maybe small.

A common way to make a small amount of money is to start a small business—your own Yoga studio, a YouTube channel, hawking merchandise, and so on. You might make it big, but the odds are you will remain small or go out of business. I can tell you from my own experience that publishing meticulous bilingual Sanskrit-English editions of the classic Yoga texts is not the road to easy riches. It's more like conducting trench warfare with a tablespoon. To be more specific, Ingram, the world's largest wholesaler of books, offers over 1300 editions of the *Bhagavad Gita*. It's Gresham's Law on steroids. The type of Yoga books that have sold well to date are the full-color anatomy manuals with cutaway asana illustrations.

To make a lot of money, to be a genuine Yoga millionaire, set yourself up as a guru. You can kick it old school with matted hair, skin smeared with ashes, and sitting on a tiger skin. You can put on a business suit and give Power-Point presentations. You can do anything; nothing is too crazy. Books, magazines, DVDs, t-shirts, essential oils; lectures, classes, intensives, retreats, initiations; levels of membership, tithing, a global network of ashrams—the opportunities are endless. A sideline of Ayurvedic products is often quite successful. Word to the wise: Don't lose your soul.

To pick just one of many, many examples,

take a subset of asanas, turn up the heat to 105 degrees Fahrenheit, flog the hell out of it, and then buy yourself a dozen Rolls-Royces. That's Bikram Yoga.

To make a stupendous amount of money, to be a genuine Yoga billionaire, I really know of only one way, and that's to design, make, and market stretchy clothes that give a woman a nice-looking ass. Lululemon is the best example. Multiply the price-per-share times the number of shares outstanding and you'll see that LULU (its ticker symbol) has a market capitalization of tens of billions of dollars. It is one of the 500 most valuable companies in the world. And LULU has many competitors. (One of them is even named Hard Tail, just in case the purpose of these clothes is not clear enough for you.)

Speaking of billionaires, you may have heard of the Koch (rhymes with "coke") brothers and their privately held conglomerate, Koch Industries. They like to invest in products fundamental to our modern way of life, but not directly facing the consumer. Lycra (also known generically as Spandex and other names), the basic stretchy material that goes into Yoga pants, was invented by DuPont in 1958. DuPont sold Lycra to Koch Industries in 2003, and Koch still retains a minority interest.

So woke, but also Koch.

(The clothes are also difficult to recycle.)

न वेषधारणं सिद्धेः कारणं न च तत्कथा ।
क्रियैव कारणं सिद्धेः सत्यमेतन्न संशयः ॥

Success is achieved neither by wearing the right clothes nor by talking about it. Practice alone brings success. This is the truth, without a doubt.

Yoga and Religion

This could have been an endless chapter, but I'll get right to the point. Yoga is not a religion, Yoga is not at the core of a religion, a religion is not at the core of Yoga. Yoga is a phenomenon of Indic civilization, and it now inhabits a global civilization, but it always was and remains its own thing. Nor is it a philosophy, in the sense of something you just read and think and talk about. It's something you do and experience. Think of it as open-source software for the soul.

Yoga shares concepts (e.g., karma, samsara) with Buddhism, Jainism, Tantrism, village religions, and the rest of the Indian mental world. It is closest to what is now called Hinduism but was

not at the core of Hinduism. It was extra-Vedic
instead of Vedic, heterodox more than orthodox, egalitarian rather than caste-obsessed,
practiced more in the forest than in the home or
temples, wild instead of puritanical, left-handed
instead of right.

So Yoga is Indian, but it can be—and is—
practiced everywhere in the world by Catholics,
the Orthodox, and Protestants; Sunnis, Shias,
and Sufis; Vaishnavas, Shaivas, and Shaktas;
Buddhists, Daoists, Sikhs, Parsis, Jews, and
Jains. It is also practiced by lapsed Catholics,
Post-Protestants, secular Muslims, modern
Hindus, the ever-burgeoning "spiritual but not
religious" cohort, agnostics, the uncategoriz-
able, and more. (Yoga is probably not for ob-
durate atheists; one needs an open heart and an
open mind.)

Next, gurus. Almost any Yoga book will tell
you not to attempt Yoga without guidance, that
a guru is essential, that the guru is next to God,
and indeed, that the guru *is* God.

But of course, they would say that, wouldn't they? It's in their self-interest.

Let's do a reality check. They've grown up breathing the same air and drinking the same water as we do, reading the same books and hearing the same lectures. They were born in our time and on this same Earth. There is no verifiable unbroken chain of gurus going back to antiquity. As we have seen, most teachers descend from two twentieth-century figures.

So beware of tyrants, cult leaders, frauds, clowns, and sex offenders. Find someone honest, competent, and good-hearted. Also keep in mind that your teacher, your fellow students, and you yourself are all still just healthy primates practicing potentially sexually stimulating exercises. Don't be astonished if there is some monkey business.

Finally, there have been many proclamations over the last century that God is dead, God is back, religion is dead, religion is back, secularism is the future, and secularism is the past. Does any of this matter to Yoga? Perhaps not as much as you might think. My guess is that Yoga can slough off religion almost entirely and we will proceed like argonauts of the infinite. Which brings us to our next chapter on science.

क्रियायुक्तस्य सिद्धिः स्यादक्रियस्य कथं भवेत् ।
न शास्त्रपाठमात्रेण योगसिद्धिः प्रजायते ॥

The practitioner will succeed; the nonpractitioner will not. Success in Yoga is not achieved by merely reading books.

Yoga and Science

If you pick up most any classic Yoga text, it won't be long before you start running into terms like bile, phlegm, humors, and so on. It dawns on you pretty quickly that you're not in Kansas anymore. In fact, you're not even in the modern world anymore. You're in the medieval world.

Yoga is premodern in two ways. The first is simply that it chronologically predates our current modern era. The second is that, following Thomas Kuhn, there is no dominant paradigm, a characteristic of modern science. Indeed, there is a lack of consensus on just about everything: the number of steps in Yoga, what each step consists of, what the steps are called, what is the goal of Yoga and how is it described, and even the definition of Yoga itself. There are a lot of people claiming to have found the One True Yoga, but they don't agree with each other.

Does this mean Yoga is obsolete and worthless? No, I don't think so.

First, why does it deeply appeal to hundreds of millions of modern humans around the world—often the most highly educated members of their societies? I think because Yoga is a treasure chest, a toolbox of time-tested mental and experiential practices. People sense and experience its intrinsic worth.

Second, Yoga is prescientific. It is not nonscientific. It is not antiscientific. Modernization has already begun. I believe we're halfway through a transition period, lasting perhaps four centuries, simultaneously looking back to the original texts and looking forward to a scientific understanding. It's exciting!

Here are just a few (of many) questions to

ask. Every yogi since the beginning has been a *Homo sapiens sapiens*, so biology in the larger scheme of things is mostly a constant. Which facets of Yoga have a biological basis and which do not? Are chakras really real, or are they more like phlogiston? What about the promised supernatural powers? The old nineteenth-century approach was to sweep them under the rug in embarrassment, the current take is more of a strategic ambiguity, but the scientific approach would be: Find out!

Haven't experiments already been done? In fact, they have. Experiments have been conducted for over a century in Lonavala (near Mumbai) and now around the world. Think of a meditating yogi in a sealed chamber to measure respiration, or a yogi in an MRI machine to compare a baseline mental state with a meditative state.

Results have been inconclusive for several reasons. One is that Yoga research has been a cottage industry compared to, say, the war on cancer.

A second is that science and medicine are changing rapidly and still have a long way to go, so the best hypotheses, experiments, and results are ahead of us. We're more at the Wright Brothers stage than the SpaceX stage. Are you following me? Yoga is preparadigmatic and the branches and twigs of science interfacing with consciousness are also preparadigmatic. They will co-evolve over the next 175 years. Neither is fixed.

A third is that while anything can be approached scientifically, it may not be possible to devise experiments that yield usable results. This is really hard stuff. Think of the difficulty of comprehending the brain. The mind. Consciousness. Health in its widest sense. How long before these are fully understood? Decades? Centuries? Never?

Consider yourself an explorer of the soul or a researcher of the infinite. Let's find out together what's real, what's fantasy, what's beneficial, what's harmful. And to be very blunt, what to keep and what to toss. (Don't worry, ancient and medieval Yoga will never fully go away.) In a way, these decisions are already being crowd-sourced. Everyone practices asanas, most practice breathing, fewer still meditate, and almost no one practices the purificatory exercises.

I think the dialectic between Yoga and science will produce something open and robust instead of something closed, fragile, and fragmentary.

खमध्ये कुरु चात्मानमात्ममध्ये च खं कुरु ।
सर्वं च खमयं कृत्वा न किंचिदपि चिन्तयेत् ॥

Center the self in space and space in the self.
Make everything space, then don't think
of anything.

Yoga and Society

We ended the first chapter around 1950. The last 75 years have seen the Cold War, the Space Age, the Information Age, the third and fourth waves of decolonization (the erstwhile Third World and Soviet Union), the population bomb and incipient demographic collapse, globalization and (perhaps) incipient deglobalization, urbanization, pollution, climate change, and biodiversity loss, just to mention a few of the highlights. The scale and speed and impact of all this has been so massive that a new geological epoch has been declared—the Anthropocene.

Ditto Yoga. It has gone from a fringe activity to part of a counterculture to part of mainstream

culture. The disciples of Sivananda and Krishnamacharya spread around the world, founding
globe-spanning institutions and teaching tens
of thousands of students. Richard Hittleman
and Lilias Folan produced hundreds of instruc-
tional episodes for American television audiences. Cheap paperbacks flooded the market.
The Beatles took up Transcendental Medita-
tion, moved to Rishikesh for a time, and added
Indian classical instrumentation to their music.
Then came even more gurus, teachers, TTCs,
classes, ashrams, and studios. Magazines sprang
up. Cheap airfare to and from India. Methods
and schools of thought proliferated. Then the
Internet, smartphones, apps, and YouTube.
Yoga has survived and thrived. Exploded, really.

Why? And after 2500 years, why now?

First I'll round up the usual suspects, then
look at Yoga as an emergent phenomenon, and
finally look at the work of the social scientist
Ronald F. Inglehart.

Yoga feels good, giving a glowing feeling of

warmth, peace, relaxation, energy, and tranquility. Yoga is good for your physical health, keeping you supple, flexible, resilient, and improving your balance and circulation. Yoga is good for your mental health, making you blissful, calm, observant, and less needful of drugs and alcohol. Yoga is experiential, not just dozing off in a pew. Yoga is convenient since you need just the tiniest bit of space. Yoga is free—once you know how to do it, you are good to go. Yoga is both solitary, if you prefer to practice alone, and convivial, if you enjoy going to classes or practicing with friends. So, feels great, good for all of you, easy, free, and fun. In light of all this, perhaps the surprising thing is that it isn't even more popular!

It's quite striking how Yoga has emerged from almost total obscurity, disdain, ridicule, and indifference. It has been a grassroots, word-of-mouth, bottom-up phenomenon, without government support, without institutional support, without a formal clergy or faculty, without standardization or a dominant paradigm—just self-selected teachers and self-selected students self-organizing. Triumphing over malign neglect, this type of groundswell can be formidable.

So Yoga emerged, but why did it resonate? Why was the ground so fertile? I think much of the answer can be found in the work of Inglehart, particularly his monograph *Cultural Evolution: People's Motivations are Changing, and Reshaping the World*, which draws on decades of work and hundreds of thousands of interviews around the globe. He argues that post-WWII economic and physical security gains brought a shift from materialist to postmaterialist values, from survival values to self-expression values, with less violence and more democracy. When people are more secure, they become more outgoing and tolerant and show less deference to authority and hierarchical institutions. A knowledge society fosters spiritual concerns.

It's almost as if Yoga was tailor-made for this moment.

अन्तः शून्यो बहिः शून्यः शून्यः कुम्भ इवाम्बरे ।
अन्तः पूर्णो बहिः पूर्णः पूर्णः कुम्भ इवार्णवे ॥

Empty within, empty without, empty like a pot
in space. Full within, full without, full like a pot
in the ocean.

Yoga and the Future

We ended the previous chapter around 2025. The post-WWII era has been one of unprecedented prosperity. This economic and physical security created a fertile environment for Yoga to flourish in. Sometimes Yoga has been a fad and sometimes a trend (and oftentimes both), and has therefore waxed and waned, but it has emerged out of nowhere to become a global phenomenon.

What will the next 175 years bring? Let's start with where we are now and assume more of the same, with special attention to political ramifications and scientific possibilities. That's a sunny future. Next, we'll look at some possible troubling developments. That would be a cloudy future. Finally, what if things go badly wrong, say a civilizational collapse? That would be a stormy future indeed.

Where are we now as a planetary civilization? Cast your mind back to high-school physics and the formula F=ma, or force equals mass times acceleration. For mass substitute demography (eight billion people and growing), for acceleration substitute technology (5G headed to 6G, EUV semiconductor lithography headed to one nanometer), and for force substitute civilizational change. We're headed for *rapid change at scale* that will bring opportunities and challenges, pluses and minuses.

If our world holds together, Yoga will continue to grow and contribute to it. Yoga has a zero carbon footprint (unless you're constantly jetting off to Bali or Goa to chill) and it helps people cope with the stress of modern life, from lowering blood pressure to providing a circle of friends to giving meaning to life.

Becoming an ever-larger global phenomenon is going to bring growing pains and possibilities not yet thought of. So far, Yoga's relations with the state have been mostly about how to interface with the healthcare industry. Is it preventive care? What does insurance cover? What organizations should be recognized? How should practitioners be certified? Can it be taught in public schools? Which agency should do the regulating? Should Yoga be divested of its Indian traditions? These conversations give me a bit of claustrophobia but are probably unavoidable.

As for the most relevant state, the Republic of India, Yoga does have a history, through Aurobindo and others, with a muscular Indian nationalism. The narratives about Yoga, Indic civilization, Hinduism, and the Republic of India will be continually examined, reassessed, and reconfigured. As the Republic of India makes its 150-year journey from prostrate object of pity (1950) to full-spectrum superpower (2100), will it ever feel tempted or compelled to project soft or hard power to protect yogis around the world? How odd to think that Yoga could have the backing of a temporal superpower! This strikes me as very unlikely, but it's possible. On the flip side, just as China felt threatened by Falun Gong, so too the Republic of India could feel threatened by a future Yoga movement and persecute it.

What could unite yogis internationally? We just mentioned Yoga's link to Indian nationalism, which began as an anti-colonial struggle. Could yogis join the fifth and final wave of decolonization, for example, of Palestine? Both movements are decidedly bottom-up and unpopular with the establishment. This also strikes me as unlikely. Yet it could happen.

Another hopeful possibility derives from the fact that Yoga is intrinsically free and historically egalitarian. Could Yoga be the champion of the 99%? Nothing about it inherently restricts it to upper-middle-class women. The coming AI society may well be even more un-equal and would benefit from a counterweight.

Alas, although there are always reasons for hope, Yoga's record on going from lifestyle to liberation is quite poor so far, with the path from a crunchy lifestyle to alt-right beliefs being a real thing. Ditto vaccine skepticism. Ditto health supplements.

If and when Yoga is politically mobilized, the one certain ramification is blowback. Fundamentalists, purists, conservatives, and establishments will not be happy.

As for scientific possibilities, they will be transformational. Very roughly speaking, I would say that Yoga is halfway through its encounter with science, with the nineteenth and twentieth centuries behind us and the twenty-first and twenty-second ahead. Halfway chronologically, but almost all the work is ahead of us, waiting on more advanced instrumentation, improved computational abilities, and conceptual breakthroughs. Anyone who follows even just the latest health news knows that we are not remotely close to having everything nailed down.

Of particular note are the Indological possibilities of AI. We may never get to the point of tossing a Sanskrit manuscript into the front end and a fully processed text coming out the back end, but we should go a considerable way toward scanning, recognizing, comprehending, translating, and annotating a text—even without a large corpus of good translations. Perhaps the AIs will recognize the good stuff and deprecate the bad stuff, automating critical editions. (Or at least throw in their two cents when you ask for their opinions.) Beyond that, will they start writing their own verses and texts, drawing on all philosophical, medical, and scientific knowledge bases everywhere? Will they write them in Sanskrit?

As a science fiction writer of no note, I would be remiss if I didn't mention Arthur C. Clarke's classic 1953 short story "The Nine Billion Names of God," in which Tibetan monks use a mainframe computer to calculate all the permutations and combinations of the name of God, thereby bringing an end to the universe. I don't think the AIs can or will end the universe, but they might try to bring an end to us humans. Since Yoga is so beneficial to humans, if you start to notice a diffuse and subtle attempt to bring Yoga into disrepute, it could be the AIs preparing the information battlefield.

Continuing pressing into the realm of science fiction, as we humans become more and more enmeshed with hardware and software systems, will Yoga help us sort out what is useful and what is not, what is bad and what is good, what is truly human and what is not?

A parting thought on science, Yoga, and the future: The urge to know and experience should make us resilient when we make first contact with an alien civilization. A lot of worldviews will shatter, but we'll be supple and good to go.

This future is sunny.

Next, serious dislocation. It could be slow

or fast, partial or complete. The Anthropocene may be short-lived indeed. How will Yoga cope?

Going back to Inglehart, the stresses of disease, inequality, immigration, and reaction to new values could (in fact, have already) result in a society less open to change and new ideas. Think of the rise of right-wing populist parties around the world. The growth of Yoga would slow down or stop.

Yogis could succumb to the lure of sex, power, fame, wealth, drugs—all the usual suspects. Indeed, the track record in this regard is not good, which is why I cautioned about gurus earlier. So many have come and gone.

Another self-inflicted wound would be the splintering of Yoga itself. Due to its decentralized and egalitarian character, it has always contained a diversity of thought and practice. But now we have modern branding, social media, and big money at stake. It could create a cacophony.

When I was growing up, a major concern

was overpopulation. A growing concern now is demographic collapse. Yoga has both ascetics and householders, so it should be able to thrive in either anti-natal or pro-natal environments.

This future is cloudy.

Those are some of the slow and partial changes. But what if the world really collapsed, or endured a series of collapses? Once multiple tipping points coincide, things can unravel quickly. And there are many candidates: the singularity, nuclear exchange, climate change, global war, pandemic, asteroid impact, volcanic mega-eruption, bioterrorism.

I believe that Yoga works either way: dealing with the stress of modernity, but also dealing with the scarcities of the collapse of modernity. All you need is a bit of space, bhai.

If it gets really, really ugly, yogis have militarized before, and yogis have lived in a medieval world before. We'll be good either way—a steady light in dark times.

This future is stormy.

Who has the vote for a prosperous future or for collapse? Everyone has a vote and a voice, especially you, the person reading this book. The future of Yoga is before us. You can help create it. It's in your hands.

Even the sky is not the limit. We are living in a liminal space, looking back to Sanskrit texts and pushing out into the solar system. Perhaps it would be wise to bring something primordial along with us.

This is my belief. Drawing on 25 centuries of experience, free, open to all, open to new knowledge, now and in the future, as we practice, the infinite, the mystery, the divine, the way, will become clear.

Yoga is our path.

Now is our time.

उत्साहात्साहसाद्धैर्यात्तत्त्वज्ञानाच्च निश्चयात् ।
जनसङ्गपरित्यागात्षड्भिर्योगः प्रसिद्धयति ॥

Yoga succeeds by these six: enthusiasm, openness, courage, knowledge of the truth, determination, and solitude.

Author

BRIAN DANA AKERS began practicing Yoga at age twelve, learning Sanskrit at seventeen, and working in publishing at twenty-three. You can find out more about him at brianakers.com.

YOGAVIDYA.COM is dedicated to publishing excellent and affordable books about Yoga. It is completely independent of any commercial, governmental, educational, or religious institutions.